Editor
Dona Herweck Rice

Editorial Project Manager
Evan D. Forbes, M.S. Ed.

Editor in Chief
Sharon Coan, M.S. Ed.

Illustrator
Sue Fullam

Cover Artist
Keith Vasconcelles

Art Director
Elayne Roberts

Imaging
Alfred Lau

Product Manager
Phil Garcia

Publishers
Rachelle Cracchiolo, M.S. Ed.
Mary Dupuy Smith, M.S. Ed.

Critical Thinkir

USA Brain Teasers

Author

Carol Eichel

Teacher Created Materials, Inc.
6421 Industry Way
Westminster, CA 92683
www.teachercreated.com
©1995 Teacher Created Materials, Inc.
Reprinted, 2004
Made in U.S.A.
ISBN-1-55734-547-3

TABLE OF CONTENTS

INTRODUCTION

The *Brain Teasers* series provides ways to exercise and develop brain power! Each page stands alone and can be used as a quick and easy filler activity. The pages can be distributed to students as individual worksheets or made into transparencies for presentation to the entire class at once. The activities are especially useful in helping students develop:

- Logic and other critical thinking skills.
- Creative thinking skills.
- Research skills.
- Spelling skills.
- General vocabulary skills.
- General knowledge skills.

This U.S.A. activity book pays particular attention to the fabulous country in which we live. Along with a United States social studies curriculum, the activities here can be invaluable in introducing and reinforcing knowledge. They can also be used just for fun.

Great care has been taken in collecting accurate data for this book. As much as possible, the most current data has been used.

We hope you and your students will have great fun learning more about the country in which we live — the United States of America.

WHICH PRESIDENT?

1. Which president was nicknamed "Honest Abe"? _____

2. Which president was called the "Father of the Constitution"?

    _____

3. Which president and his wife were the first to occupy the White House in Washington D.C.? _____

4. Which future president was the author of the "Declaration of Independence"? _____

5. Which president was the only one to serve two nonconsecutive terms of office? _____

6. Which president was nicknamed "Old Rough and Ready"?

    _____

7. Which president was assassinated in Ford's Theater? _____

8. Which two presidents are buried in Arlington National Cemetery?

    _____

9. Which president served more than two terms? _____

10. Which president was in office when the White House was set on fire?

    _____

11. Which president was the grandson of another president?

    _____

12. Which president was the shortest? _____

13. Which President never married? _____

14. Which president was the first to talk to a man on the moon?

    _____

15. Which five presidents were left-handed? _____

    _____

DO YOU KNOW?

1. Which president was the son of a former president?

   _____

2. For which president was the teddy bear named? _____

3. Which president was called the "Accidental President"?

   _____

4. Which was the first president born in a log cabin? _____

5. Which president's family farm was named Mt. Vernon?

   _____

6. Which president was a movie star before becoming a president?

   _____

7. Who was America's first vice-president? _____

8. Which president is pictured on the two-dollar bill? _____

9. Which president was elected to four terms of office?

   _____

10. Who was the only person to serve as vice president and then president, who was not elected to either office.

    _____

11. Which president gave "The Gettysburg Address"? _____

12. What was President Jefferson's first name? _____

13. Which president's first two initials were U.S.?_____

14. Which president was the first to resign from office? _____

15. Which president caught a cold at his inauguration and died of pneumonia a month later? _____

4

PRESIDENTIAL STUMPERS

Use the names of the presidents to answer these questions humorously. The first one has been done for you.

1. Which president was the most honest? _____ Truman _____

2. Which president was the slowest? _____

3. Which president was irritated by his child? _____

4. Which president was popular at a service station? _____

5. Which president was the namesake of a popular cat?

   _____

6. Which president sewed clothing? _____

7. Which president took care of the laundry? _____

8. Which president was helpful in fixing a flat tire? _____

9. Which president was often cold? _____

10. Which president cleaned the carpets? _____

PRESIDENTIAL FILL-IN

Fill in the names of U.S. presidents in the blanks below. Use the names within the word bank.

Word Bank

Monroe	Nixon	Madison
Lincoln	Wilson	Washington
Adams	Bush	Eisenhower
Reagan	Ford	Roosevelt
Grant	Filmore	Jefferson
Taft	Kennedy	Cleveland

PRESIDENT'S FIRST NAMES

Listed below are some last names of former presidents. Write each President's first name on the blank.

1. _____ Adams

2. _____ Eisenhower

3. _____ Reagan

4. _____ Jefferson

5. _____ Nixon

6. _____ Lincoln

7. _____ Carter

8. _____ Hoover

9. _____ Roosevelt

10. _____ Washington

11. _____ Coolidge

12. _____ Cleveland

13. _____ Grant

14. _____ Taylor

15. _____ Harrison

16. _____ Truman

17. _____ Buchanan

18. _____ Polk

19. _____ Garfield

20. _____ Johnson

SCRAMBLED NAMES

The names of fifteen U.S. presidents have been split into two-letter segments. The letters in each segment are in order, but the segments have been scrambled. In each group, put the pieces together to identify a president.

1. OW IG EI ER DW SE HT NH   _____

2. LI LL MC WI ON IA NT   _____

3. LD RD GE FO RA   _____

4. EN RT VA MA NB IN UR   _____

5. LD AN RO AG RE NA   _____

6. GE CA CO LV OL IN ID   _____

7. GE IN ON GE WA OR SH GT   _____

8. PI FR CE IN ER AN KL   _____

9. IN ON BE HA NJ IS RR AM   _____

10. RA CO ML AB LN IN HA   _____

11. OR SH GE BU GE   _____

12. SE SG NT UL RA YS   _____

13. RI DN ON CH IX AR   _____

14. SE YR LT TE OO DD VE   _____

15. SM IS JA ON ME AD   _____

PRESIDENTS OF THE UNITED STATES

Use the information on this page to complete the next page.

	Name	Born	Place of Birth	Died	Years Lived
1.	George Washington	2/22/1732	VA	12/14/1799	----------------------
2.	John Adams	10/30/1735	MA	7/4/1826	----------------------
3.	Thomas Jefferson	4/13/1743	VA	7/4/1826	----------------------
4.	James Madison	3/16/1751	VA	6/28/1836	----------------------
5.	James Monroe	4/28/1758	VA	7/4/1831	----------------------
6.	John Q. Adams	7/11/1767	MA	2/23/1848	----------------------
7.	Andrew Jackson	3/15/1767	SC	6/8/1845	----------------------
8.	Martin Van Buren	12/5/1782	NY	7/24/1862	----------------------
9.	William Harrison	2/9/1773	VA	4/4/1841	----------------------
10.	John Tyler	3/29/1790	VA	1/18/1862	----------------------
11.	James Polk	11/2/1795	NC	6/15/1849	----------------------
12.	Zachary Taylor	11/24/1784	VA	7/9/1850	----------------------
13.	Millard Fillmore	1/7/1800	NY	3/8/1874	----------------------
14.	Franklin Pierce	11/23/1804	NH	10/8/1869	----------------------
15.	James Buchanan	4/23/1791	PA	6/1/1868	----------------------
16.	Abraham Lincoln	2/12/1809	KY	4/15/1865	----------------------
17.	Andrew Johnson	12/29/1808	NC	7/31/1875	----------------------
18.	Ulysses S. Grant	4/27/1822	OH	7/23/1885	----------------------
19.	Rutherford B. Hayes	10/4/1822	OH	1/17/1893	----------------------
20.	James Garfield	11/19/1831	OH	9/19/1881	----------------------
21.	Chester Arthur	10/5/1830	VT	11/18/1886	----------------------
22.	Grover Cleveland	3/18/1837	NJ	6/24/1908	----------------------
23.	Benjamin Harrison	8/20/1833	OH	3/13/1901	----------------------
24.	Grover Cleveland	3/18/1837	NJ	6/24/1908	----------------------
25.	William McKinley	1/29/1843	OH	9/14/1901	----------------------
26.	Theodore Roosevelt	10/27/1858	NY	1/6/1919	----------------------
27.	William Taft	9/15/1857	OH	3/8/1930	----------------------
28.	Woodrow Wilson	12/28/1856	VA	2/3/1924	----------------------
29.	Warren Harding	11/2/1865	OH	8/2/1923	----------------------
30.	Calvin Coolidge	7/4/1872	VT	1/5/1933	----------------------
31.	Herbert Hoover	8/10/1874	IA	10/20/1964	----------------------
32.	Franklin Roosevelt	1/30/1882	NY	4/12/1945	----------------------
33.	Harry Truman	5/8/1884	MO	12/26/1972	----------------------
34.	Dwight Eisenhower	10/14/1890	TX	3/28/1969	----------------------
35.	John F. Kennedy	5/29/1917	MA	11/22/1963	----------------------
36.	Lyndon B. Johnson	8/27/1908	TX	1/22/1973	----------------------
37.	Richard Nixon	1/9/1913	CA	4/22/1994	----------------------
38.	Gerald Ford	7/14/1913	NB		----------------------
39.	Jimmy Carter	10/1/1924	GA		----------------------
40.	Ronald Reagan	2/6/1911	IL		----------------------
41.	George Bush	6/12/1924	MA		----------------------
42.	Bill Clinton	8/19/1946	AR		----------------------

PRESIDENTS OF THE UNITED STATES (CONT.)

1. Find the age of each president at his death. (Some presidents are still living.) _____

2. Which presidents died on July 4? _____

3. Who was born on January 30, 1882? _____

4. In which month were the most presidents born? _____

5. Which president was born in Illinois? _____

6. From how many different states have the presidents come?

   _____

7. How many presidents are still living? _____

8. Which two presidents were born in 1767? _____

9. In what state was Grover Cleveland born? _____

10. How many presidents were born in Virginia? _____

11. Which president was the youngest to die? _____

12. When was James Buchanan's birthday? _____

13. How many presidents were born in the twentieth century?

    _____

14. How many presidents have died in the twentieth century?

    _____

PRESIDENTIAL NICKNAMES

Match the former presidents to their famous nicknames.

1. Dwight Eisenhower   Accidental President

2. Thomas Jefferson   Big Bill

3. Franklin Roosevelt   F.D.R.

4. William Harrison   Father of His Country

5. Abraham Lincoln   Father of the Constitution

6. George Washington   Father of the Declaration of Independence

7. Andrew Jackson   Honest Abe

8. Zachary Taylor   Ike

9. Richard Nixon   Old Hickory

10. Theodore Roosevelt   Old Tippecanoe

11. James Madison   Rough Rider

12. William Taft   The Dark Horse

13. John Tyler   Tricky Dick

14. James Polk   Give 'Em Hell Harry

15. Harry Truman   Old Rough and Ready

PRESIDENT NAME FIND

In the word find below are the last names of the first forty-two presidents of the United States. As you find their names, circle them and then list them on the lines below.

```
W I L S O H O O V E R E C P O L K E J
A D A M S A G A R F I E L D N J E A E
S V D S O R R N N E K I I O W O N G F
H A A J N D A E J D R S N T I H N J F
I N M R L I N C O L N E T N L N E A E
N B S E B N T J H Y E N O K S P D C R
G U R A U G F E N C W H N L O O Y K S
T R E G R F B U S H O O L I N P R S O
O E A A E I S E O H H W M A D I S O N
N N T N N I X O N R A E O S R E O N A
F L A N O B U R B U R R N C O R O N H
A R Y C X A T D U T R R R O O C A R A
F I L L M O R E C H I A O O S E R C R
T L O E N S U N H A S S E L E O T A R
Y M R V I E M O A F O R D I V H H R I
L O T E F T A T N M N W R D E N U T S
E R H L A Y N H A Y E S E G L E R E O
R E T A F T G I N H S A W E T S I R N
J O H N S O N N M C K I N L E Y E E C
C K S D O N P I E R O O S E V E L T R
```

_____   _____   _____
_____   _____   _____
_____   _____   _____
_____   _____   _____
_____   _____   _____
_____   _____   _____
_____   _____   _____
_____   _____   _____
_____   _____   _____
_____   _____   _____
_____   _____   _____

U.S. PRESIDENTS

Name the president who:

1. Never lived in the White House. _____

2. Was born on the Fourth of July. _____

3. Arranged the Louisiana Purchase. _____

4. Was nicknamed Ike. _____

5. Weighed over 300 pounds. _____

6. Was sworn into office on an airplane. _____

7. Was the only president to get married in the White House.

   _____

8. Was president during the Great Depression and WWII.

   _____

9. Summed up his policy by saying, "Speak softly, and carry a big stick."

   _____

10. Resigned from office. _____

11. Served the shortest time in office. _____

12. Also served as chief justice. _____

13. Is pictured on the one-dollar bill. _____

14. Had the most children. _____

15. Was president during the Civil War. _____

FAMOUS QUOTES

Identify the originator of each famous quote.

1. "The buck stops here." _____

2. "I have a dream . . ." _____

3. "Give me liberty or give me death." _____

4. "I never met a man I didn't like." _____

5. "O say, can you see . . ." _____

6. "Mr. Watson, come here. I want you." _____

7. "That's one small step for man; one giant leap for mankind."

   _____

8. "The Eagle has landed." _____

9. "The only thing we have to fear is fear itself."

   _____

10. "Ask not what your country can do for you; ask what you can do for your country." _____

11. "A penny saved is a penny earned." _____

12. "I have not yet begun to fight." _____

13. "You can't fool all the people all the time." _____

14. "I shall return." _____

15. ". . . government by the people, for the people, . . ."

   _____

　　　　14

EXPLORERS AND ADVENTURERS

1. Who "discovered" America in 1492? _____

2. Who was the first person to walk on the moon?_____

3. Who was the first known person to sail completely around the world?
   _____

4. Who became the first American in outer space?_____

5. In 1620, what group of people landed at Plymouth Rock?
   _____

6. Who was the first American to orbit the earth in a space vehicle?
   _____

7. Who was the first American woman to go into space?_____

8. For whom is America named?_____

9. Which two explorers led the expedition over the Rocky Mountains to the
   Pacific? _____

10. Who was the educator selected to be the first teacher in space?
    _____

11. Who discovered and sailed up the St. Lawrence River?
    _____

12. Which two Americans were the first to reach the North Pole?
    _____

13. What Native American guide explored with Lewis and Clark?
    _____

14. Which two French-Canadians explored the northern Mississippi basin?
    _____

15. What Norse explorer was probably the first European to reach mainland
    North America? _____

WHO IS IT?

Cut out the individual pieces to form the portrait of a famous American.

FAMOUS WOMEN

Match these women to their major accomplishments. Put the letter of the accomplishment before the corresponding name.

_____ 1. Harriet Tubman

_____ 2. Harriet Beecher Stowe

_____ 3. Grandma Moses

_____ 4. Juliette Gordon Low

_____ 5. Shirley Chisholm

_____ 6. Pearl S. Buck

_____ 7. Mary McLeod Bethune

_____ 8. Clara Barton

_____ 9. Louisa May Alcott

_____ 10. Susan B. Anthony

_____ 11. Jane Addams

_____ 12. Amelia Earhart

_____ 13. Helen Hayes

_____ 14. Helen Keller

_____ 15. Victoria C. Woodhull

A. social worker and humanitarian

B. primitive painter

C. novelist and writer

D. stage and screen actress

E. author of *The Good Earth*

F. Aviator

G. author of *Little Women*

H. educator who worked to improve educational opportunities for blacks

I. significant "conductor" of the Underground Railroad

J. first woman to run for president of the U.S.

K. first African American woman in the U.S. Congress

L. founded the Girl Scouts of America

M. founded the American Red Cross

N. overcame physical handicaps; helped thousands of handicapped people lead fuller lives

O. reformer and leader in the American woman's suffrage movement

TWO TO ONE

The answer to each of the following items is the name of a U.S. personality. Take one letter from each column to find your answer. The first has been done for you.

1.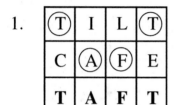

T	I	L	T
C	A	F	E
T	**A**	**F**	**T**

6.

F	A	R	M
C	O	L	D

2.

P	A	L	E
L	O	O	K

7.

Y	O	Y	O	S
H	A	T	E	D

3.

G	R	I	N	D
A	W	A	I	T

8.

B	A	C	K
W	E	L	L

4.

R	U	S	H
B	A	T	H

9.

C	L	I	C	K
A	L	A	R	M

5.

F	A	S	T	E	R
C	E	R	E	A	L

10.

T	H	R	E	E
M	O	U	S	E

11.

K	E	L	L	O	G
R	U	N	N	E	R

WHO IS IT?

Fill in the blanks to complete the five letter words. When read from top to bottom, the word made by the center letters will spell the name of a famous U.S. personality. The first one has been done for you.

```
1.    C  H  A  N  T
      F  A  D  E  S
      C  L  A  M  P
      G  A  M  E  S
      W  I  S  E  R

2.    F  I  __  T  Y
      B  L  __  W  S
      C  U  __  L  Y
      W  I  __  E  R

3.    B  O  __  B  S
      C  R  __  M  P
      B  A  __  L  Y
      W  H  __  L  E
      L  O  __  E  R
      C  R  __  S  S
      W  I  __  K  S

4.    P  A  __  E  S
      C  R  __  F  T
      P  A  __  T  Y
      F  I  __  T  Y
      D  R  __  N  K
      F  L  __  S  H
      B  U  __  L  Y
      W  I  __  E  N

5.    R  A  __  A  H
      C  H  __  W  S
      J  I  __  F  Y
      R  A  __  T  S
      S  H  __  L  L
      B  A  __  K  S
      B  A  __  T  E
      C  H  __  R  E
      C  A  __  D  Y
```

```
6.    C  L  __  A  N
      C  L  __  M  B
      D  U  __  T  Y
      G  R  __  A  T
      G  O  __  E  R
      A  S  __  E  S
      S  T  __  N  R
      T  O  __  E  T
      C  H  __  A  Y
      D  I  __  T  Y

7.    C  L  __  M  P
      B  I  __  C  H
      C  O  __  B  S
      M  U  __  T  Y
      G  U  __  S  Y
      F  O  __  C  E
      C  H  __  K  E
      F  I  __  A  L
      A  N  __  E  R

8.    S  E  __  E  N
      D  R  __  A  D
      T  A  __  T  E
      P  A  __  E  R
      B  A  __  S  H
      P  I  __  K  S
      K  I  __  K  S
      B  L  __  M  P

9.    P  L  __  A  D
      M  A  __  A  M
      S  H  __  R  T
      P  A  __  T  E
      C  L  __  C  E
      D  A  __  C  E

10.   D  R  __  S  S
      P  L  __  N  T
      P  A  __  T  Y
      O  T  __  E  R
      G  L  __  S  S
      T  H  __  E  S
      W  I  __  C  H
```

FAMOUS AMERICANS

Write the name of the person described in each phrase below.

1. The author of *Poor Richard's Almanac* _____

2. The pioneer who planted apple trees _____

3. The writer of "The Star-Spangled Banner" _____

4. The pioneer who explored and settled Kentucky _____

5. The author of *The Sun Also Rises* and *The Old Man and the Sea*
   _____

6. The president of the Confederacy during the Civil War
   _____

7. The skillful promoter who started the Barnum and Bailey Circus
   _____

8. The first African American to play major league baseball
   _____

9. The seamstress who is said to have made the first official U.S. flag
   _____

10. The Native American who played professional baseball and football and won Olympic gold medals in track and field _____

11. The Lakota (Sioux) leader in the battle of the Little Bighorn in which Custer died _____

12. The founder of the American Red Cross _____

13. The author of *Little Women* and *Little Men* _____

14. The scientist who discovered more than 200 uses for peanuts
    _____

15. The advocate of women's suffrage who is pictured on the one-dollar coin
    _____

INVENTORS AND THEIR INVENTIONS

Write an invention from the Invention Box next to the name of the person who is responsible for it.

1. Wright Brothers _____

2. Alexander Graham Bell _____

3. Eli Whitney _____

4. Benjamin Franklin _____

5. Henry Ford _____

6. Jonas Salk _____

7. John Deere _____

8. Charles Goodyear _____

9. Elian Howe _____

10. George Eastman _____

11. Robert Fulton _____

12. Thomas Edison _____

13. Clarence Birdseye _____

14. Samuel Morse _____

15. George Pullman _____

16. George Carver _____

Invention Box

Kodak® camera	over 200 uses for the peanut	cotton gin
steel plow	first successful airplane	phonograph
quick-freezing process of preserving food	telephone	polio vaccine
vulcanization of rubber	assembly-line method of production	sewing machine
bifocal glasses	railroad sleeping car	electric telegraph
		steamboat

WASHINGTON, D.C.

1. Near what river is Washington, D.C. located?

    _____

2. In what year did the construction of the capitol begin?

    _____

3. Who drafted a design for the District of Columbia?

    _____

4. In what year was the Capitol building completed? _____

5. What two houses comprise Congress? _____

    _____

6. What do Americans call the home and office of the president?

    _____

7. Does the vice-president also live in the White House? _____

8. What are the first seven words of the preamble to the Constitution?

    _____

9. For what is the Department of Defense responsible?

    _____

10. Who is buried at Arlington National Cemetery?_____

    _____

11. Who does the Tomb of the Unknown Soldier memorialize?

    _____

12. What museum complex (the largest in the world) is located in Washington, D.C.? _____

13. What two things are made at the Bureau of Printing and Engraving?

    _____

14. The three monuments in Washington are in memory of what famous men?

    _____

15. Which president was the first to live in the White House?

    _____

STATE CAPITALS I

Listed below are the capital cities of some of the fifty states. Write the name of each state on the line next to its capital city.

1. Springfield_____

2. Columbia_____

3. Honolulu _____

4. Richmond _____

5. Montgomery _____

6. Charleston _____

7. Boston _____

8. Hartford_____

9. Albany_____

10. Phoenix _____

11. Santa Fe_____

12. Oklahoma City _____

13. Juneau _____

14. St. Paul _____

15. Montpelier_____

16. Dover_____

17. Austin _____

18. Augusta_____

19. Helena_____

20. Des Moines _____

21. Bismarck_____

22. Little Rock _____

23. Harrisburg_____

24. Carson City _____

25. Frankfort _____

STATE CAPITALS II

Listed below are the capital cities of some of the fifty states. Write the name of each state on the line next to its capital.

1. Sacramento _____

2. Trenton _____

3. Baton Rouge _____

4. Salem_____

5. Tallahassee _____

6. Lansing _____

7. Columbus _____

8. Indianapolis_____

9. Lincoln _____

10. Denver_____

11. Topeka_____

12. Pierre_____

13. Jackson _____

14. Concord_____

15. Providence_____

16. Atlanta_____

17. Salt Lake City _____

18. Madison_____

19. Raleigh _____

20. Olympia_____

21. Nashville _____

22. Boise _____

23. Jefferson City _____

24. Cheyenne_____

25. Annapolis _____

24

STATE NICKNAMES

Listed below are the nicknames of each of the fifty states. Write the name of the state on the line after the nickname.

1. Aloha State _____

2. Bluegrass State _____

3. Mountain State _____

4. Centennial State _____

5. Land of Lincoln _____

6. Cowboy State _____

7. Bay State_____

8. Granite State _____

9. Evergreen State_____

10. Yellowhammer _____

11. Ocean State_____

12. Beehive State _____

13. Sunshine State_____

14. Constitution State _____

15. Cornhusker State_____

16. Golden State _____

17. Show Me State _____

18. Peach State _____

19. Pine Tree State _____

20. Lone Star State _____

21. Old Line State_____

22. Last Frontier _____

23. Land of Enchantment _____

24. Sunflower State_____

25. Magnolia State _____

STATE NICKNAMES (CONT.)

26. Land of Opportunity
_____

27. Tar Heel State _____

28. Palmetto State _____

29. Sunshine or
Peninsula State _____

30. Mother of Presidents_____

31. Hoosier State_____

32. Keystone State _____

33. Silver State _____

34. Garden State _____

35. Grand Canyon State _____

36. Gopher State _____

37. Sooner State _____

38. Hawkeye State _____

39. Buckeye State _____

40. First State _____

41. Volunteer State _____

42. Treasure State _____

43. Green Mountains
State_____

44. American's
Dairyland_____

45. Spud State_____

46. Empire State _____

47. Beaver State _____

48. Pelican State _____

49. Sioux State _____

50. Wolverine State_____

NAME WITHIN A NAME

Each of the following names can be found within one of the fifty state or capital names. Can you think of the state or capital whose names contains the names listed below?

1. Carol _____

2. Lulu _____

3. Jeff _____

4. Diana _____

5. Tex _____

6. Paul _____

7. Kent _____

8. Art _____

9. Helen _____

10. Jack _____

11. Rich _____

12. Ida _____

13. Trent _____

14. Frank _____

15. Cal _____

16. June _____

17. Louis _____

18. Mary _____

19. Del _____

20. Charles _____

21. Ken _____

22. Anna _____

STATES ENDING IN "A"

Twenty-one of the fifty states end in the letter "A." Can you find these states in the word search below? Answers can be found across or down.

Alabama

Alaska

Arizona

California

Florida

Georgia

Indiana

Iowa

Louisiana

Minnesota

Montana

Nebraska

Nevada

North Carolina

North Dakota

Oklahoma

Pennsylvania

South Carolina

South Dakota

Virginia

West Virginia

```
N O R T H D A K O T A A L O A
O R L O U I S I A N A I I A L
R W E S T V I R G I N I A K E
T G O N F F L O R I D A N S S
H A I N R O F I L A C N N A K
C A V I R G I N I A W A E R O
A R I Z O N A O A W O I V B N
R M R M I A L A I D A S A E O
O A G O D A A R A N A I D N I
L M I N N E S O T A N U A R R
I A N T I L K A I G R O E G T
N B I A U O A M O H A L K O H
A A A N I L O R A C H T U O S
S L A A I N A V L Y S N N E P
I A S O U T H D A K O T A A C
```

PUT THEM ALL TOGETHER AND WHAT HAVE YOU GOT?

Choose one syllable from column A, one from B, and one from C to form a state composed of three syllables. Each syllable in each column may be used only once. Write the new words in column D.

Column A	Column B	Column C	Column D
Mich	kan	ho	
Ken	i	ton	
Ne	tan	ka	
A	tuck	ware	
Wash	a	sas	
I	e	y	
Mar	las	land	
Del	da	da	
Or	gin	ka	
Flor	i	a	
O	y	o	
Ar	nes	ia	
Ten	bras	gan	
Mon	hi	see	
Vir	ing	gon	

DO YOU KNOW?

1. Which state is closer to Russia than to any other state?
   _____

2. In which state is the world's largest canyon? _____

3. Which was the first state entered into the United States?
   _____

4. Which state is the only state not in North America?
   _____

5. Which state grows more wheat than any other state?
   _____

6. In which state can people see the sun rise before anyone else in the United States? _____

7. In which state are more cars and trucks built than in any other state?
   _____

8. In which state are the headquarters of the United Nations?
   _____

9. In which state did the first successful airplane flight take place?
   _____

10. In which state is the world's largest chocolate factory?
    _____

11. Which of the fifty states is the smallest? _____

12. In which state were more presidents born than in any other?
    _____

13. Which state is the only one named after a president?
    _____

14. Which state is the only state to grow coffee beans?
    _____

15. Which state has the highest mountain in the U.S.?
    _____

UNITED STATES OF AMERICA WORD FIND

List each state on the lines below as you find it in the puzzle.

```
M A S S A C H U S E T T S C R F T S N S
N U T O M A I N E H A W A O H L O O E O
P H A U V L O R M I W D U L O O R U W Y U
E A I T M I C H I G A N T O A R E A Y T
N H N H N F C O S R S E A R T I G K O H
N D I C O O Y D S O H I H A O D O S R D
S N G A R R T E O E I P N D S A N A K A
Y A R R D N A I U G N P I O E U T L H X
L I I O S I E S R Y G I T G N I D A H O
V I V L A A R L I D T S O N N N F A N T
A B I I N T T A M E O S H I I D L M I A
N K A N S A S N I L N I L O M I O O S O
I U M A A R R D S A S S O I H A R H N E
A L O C F E E S T W A S U H O N A A O R
L W Y O M I N G N A K I I O E A L L C I
A R K E D N A L Y R A M S I R T A K S H
N L C I E P L O O E I C I L L I N O I S
I E U P A D A V E N N U A S E N O P W P
L A T T S A B E R U I T N L G O Z E N M
O I N E A N A E E R G N A A O M I M N A
R G E X L A M S V E R M O N T O R O S H
A R K A N S A S G N I E K L T Z A N H W
C O T S E I L E I I V I H O N A K T A E
H E O N M S O N O R T H D A K O T A W N
T G M A N A T N O M S M N A D W S N A W
R R E Y E S R E J W E N E V O Y I A I I
O R E I O W A T N E W M E X I C O N I L
N E B R A S K A J C O N N E C T I C U T
```

_____ _____ _____ _____ _____

_____ _____ _____ _____ _____

_____ _____ _____ _____ _____

_____ _____ _____ _____ _____

_____ _____ _____ _____ _____

_____ _____ _____ _____ _____

_____ _____ _____ _____ _____

_____ _____ _____ _____ _____

_____ _____ _____ _____ _____

_____ _____ _____ _____ _____

_____ _____ _____ _____ _____

STATE SILHOUETTES

Can you identify each of the following state silhouettes?

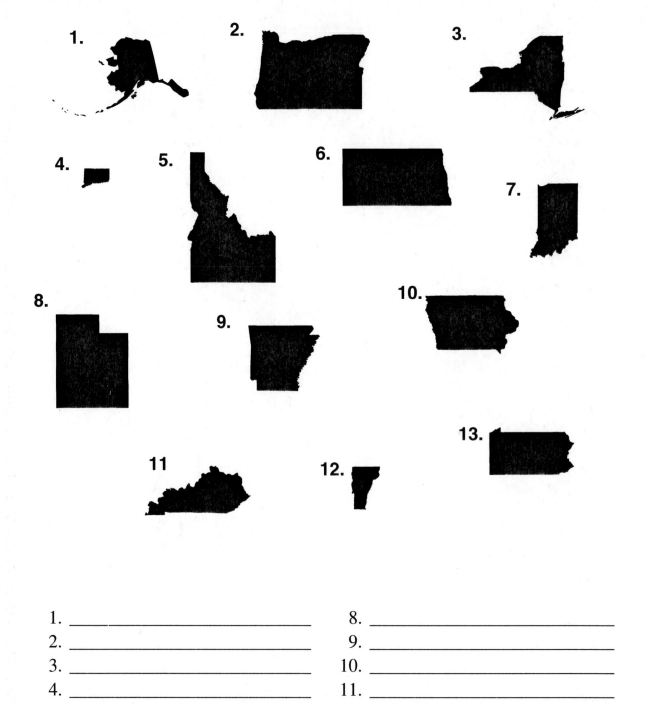

1. _____   8. _____
2. _____   9. _____
3. _____   10. _____
4. _____   11. _____
5. _____   12. _____
6. _____   13. _____
7. _____

STATE SILHOUETTES (CONT.)

14.

15.

16.

17.

18.

19.

20.

21.

22.

23.

24.

25.

26.

14. _____
15. _____
16. _____
17. _____
18. _____
19. _____
20. _____

21. _____
22. _____
23. _____
24. _____
25. _____
26. _____

STATE SILHOUETTES (CONT.)

27.

28.

29.

30.

31.

32.

33.

34.

35.

36.

37.

38.

27. _____   33. _____

28. _____   34. _____

29. _____   35. _____

30. _____   36. _____

31. _____   37. _____

32. _____   38. _____

STATE SILHOUETTES (CONT.)

39.

40.

41.

42.

43.

44.

45.

46.

47.

48.

49.

50.

39. _____   45. _____

40. _____   46. _____

41. _____   47. _____

42. _____   48. _____

43. _____   49. _____

44. _____   50. _____

THE STATUE OF LIBERTY

1. Of what metal is the Statue of Liberty made? _____

2. Which country made a gift of the statue to the United States?
_____

3. On what island in New York harbor does the statue stand?
_____

4. Why was the statue given to America? _____

5. What does Miss Liberty hold in her right hand?
_____

6. What does Miss Liberty hold in her left hand?
_____

7. What rests on Miss Liberty's head? _____

8. How high does the statue stand? _____

9. What man designed the statue? _____

10. Which president dedicated the statue? _____

11. How old is the Statue of Liberty? _____

12. When is the statue's official birthday? _____

13. What is the full name of the Statue of Liberty?
_____

14. How much does the statue weigh? _____

15. Who designed the pedestal for the statue? _____

16. What do the seven spikes on the crown symbolize?
_____

17. Who wrote the lines of verse inscribed at the base of the statue?
_____

18. For what large group of people is the statue said to be the first sight of
America? _____

WHAT IS IT?

Cut out the individual pieces to form a picture of a famous American landmark.

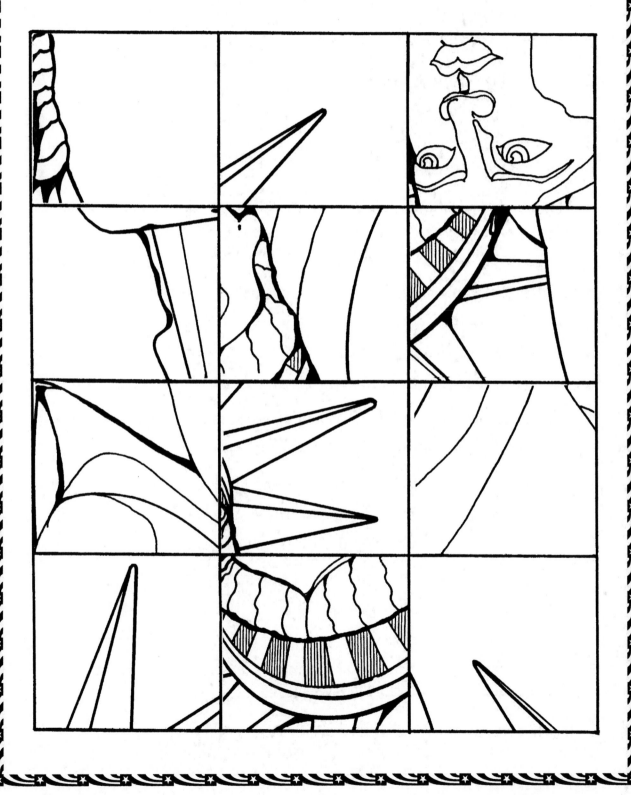

MONUMENTS AND STATUES

1. What do we call the statue on top of the Capitol Building?

   _____

2. What famous statue is located in New York City's harbor?

   _____

3. What famous memorial in Washington, D.C., is surrounded by hundreds of Japanese cherry trees? _____

4. Three monuments in Washington, D.C., were erected in honor of what men?

   _____

5. In what city would we find the Gateway Arch?

   _____

6. Where is the Tomb of the Unknown Soldier?_____

   _____

7. What does the sword in the right hand of the Statue of Freedom represent?

   _____

8. What is the tallest structure in Washington, D.C.?

   _____

9. Where is the Iwo Jima memorial statue located?

   _____

10. What does the Iwo Jima statue memorialize?

    _____

11. What monument was erected in Washington, D.C., in honor of the people who died during the war in Vietnam? _____

12. In what city would you find the Liberty Bell? _____

OUR COUNTRY'S FLAG

1. What three colors are on the United States flag?

   _____

2. What is the flag's nickname?

   _____

3. Who is said to have made the flag?

   _____

4. How many stripes are there on the flag?

   _____

5. How many red stripes are there on the flag? How Many white stripes are there? _____

6. How many stars were on the first flag?

   _____

7. What does the red on the flag represent?

   _____

8. What do the stars on the flag represent?

   _____

9. For what purpose should the flag be flown at half-mast?

   _____

10. What does the white on the flag represent?

    _____

11. What does it mean when the flag is not flying at the White House?

    _____

12. When was the U.S. flag first flown on the moon?

    _____

13. How are the stars on the current U.S. flag arranged?

    _____

14. What does the blue on the flag represent?

    _____

15. Traditionally, if a flag touches the ground, what must be done with it?

    _____

THE WHITE HOUSE

1. On what floor of the White House does the president and his or her family live? _____

2. Who was the first president to live in the White House? _____

3. What is the White House's street address? _____

4. Who designed the White House? _____

5. Where is the president's office located within the White House? _____

6. What happened to the White House in August of 1814? _____

7. How many rooms are there in the White House? _____

8. The White House was formally referred to by two other names. What were they? _____

9. Did George Washington and his family ever live in the White House? _____

10. Three rooms in the White House are named after three different colors. What are the three colors? _____

11. One of the rooms in the White House is named after which former President? _____

12. The building of the White House began in what year? _____

13. Who was the president when the British burned the White House?

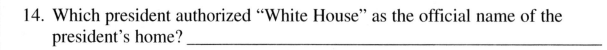

14. Which president authorized "White House" as the official name of the president's home? _____

NATIONAL LANDMARKS

In what state can each of the following landmarks be found?

1. Mt. Rushmore _____

2. Glacier National Park _____

3. Plymouth Rock _____

4. Mount St. Helens_____

5. The Everglades _____

6. The Alamo _____

7. Mt. McKinley _____

8. Yellowstone National Park _____

9. Carlsbad Caverns_____

10. Pearl Harbor _____

11. Painted Desert _____

12. Grand Tetons _____

13. Grand Canyon _____

14. Bad Lands _____

15. Niagara Falls _____

16. Old Faithful _____

17. Death Valley _____

GEOGRAPHY

1. What is the longest river in the U.S.? _____

2. From what country was the state of Alaska purchased? _____

3. What is the largest city in the U.S.? _____

4. What is the capital of the U.S.? _____

5. On which continent is the U.S. located? _____

6. What is the ocean to the west of the U.S.? _____

7. Which is the largest state? _____

8. What country is to the north of the U.S.? _____

9. What is the highest mountain in the U.S.? _____

10. Which two states lie outside the continental U.S.? _____

    _____

11. What ocean is to the east of the U.S.? _____

12. What country is to the south of the U.S.? _____

13. Which state is the only one to border only one other state?

    _____

14. What are the two largest mountain ranges in the U.S.? _____

    _____

15. In which state is the Grand Canyon located? _____

42

MOUNTAINS OF THE AMERICAS

Some of the highest mountains in America and their heights are listed below. Find the state in which each mountain is located. Then, put the mountains in height order from tallest to smallest.

Mountain	Height	State
Mt. McKinley	20,320 ft.	_____
Foraker	17,400 ft.	_____
Bona	16,421 ft.	_____
Blackburn	16,523 ft.	_____
Sanford	16,208 ft.	_____
Mt. Whitney	14,495 ft.	_____
Mt. Elbert	14,433 ft.	_____
Mt. Rainier	14,410 ft.	_____
Pike's Peak	14,110 ft.	_____
Mt. St. Elias	18,008 ft.	_____
Evans	14,264 ft.	_____
Mount Wrangell	14,005 ft.	_____
Chugach Mountains	15,300 ft.	_____
Longs Peak	14,255 ft.	_____
Mount Shasta	14,162 ft.	_____
Mauna Loa	13,677 ft.	_____
Mauna Kea	13,796 ft.	_____

Height Order

1. _____   7. _____   13. _____
2. _____   8. _____   14. _____
3. _____   9. _____   15. _____
4. _____   10. _____   16. _____
5. _____   11. _____   17. _____
6. _____   12.

LANDMARKS

Using the places listed in the Location Box below, identify where each landmark is located.

1. Walt Disney World _____

2. Washington Memorial _____

3. Golden Gate Bridge _____

4. Pearl Harbor _____

5. Plymouth Rock _____

6. Sears Tower _____

7. The Alamo _____

8. Gateway Arch _____

9. Liberty Bell _____

10. Empire State Building _____

11. Space Needle _____

12. Mt. Rushmore _____

13. Mt. McKinley _____

14. Statue of Liberty _____

15. Astrodome _____

Location Box

New York City	Seattle	St. Louis	New York City
San Francisco	Orlando	Houston	Hawaii
South Dakota	Alaska	Philadelphia	Washington, D.C.
Massachusetts	Chicago	Texas	

44

MISS LIBERTY

Fill in the blanks after the numbered problems at the bottom of the page. Once complete, match the letters to the blanks in the puzzle below to find a famous quote.

"10 1 12 2   4 2   6 11 14 3

7 1 3 2 5   6 11 14 3   16 11 11 3

6 11 14 3   9 14 5 5 13 2 5

4 8 15 15 2 15   6 2 8 3 17 1 17 10

7 11 18 3 2 8 7 9 2   19 3 2 2

1. The statue's location
17 2   6 11 3   9 8 3 18 11 3

2. Designer of the statue
18 8 3 7 9 11 13 5 1

3. A gift from this country
19 3 8 17   2

4. Color of the statue
10 3 2 2 17

5. The hand that holds the torch
3 1 10 9 7

6. The statue's island
13 1 18 2 3 7 6   1 15 13 8 17 5

7. The metal of the statue
11 16 16 2 3

8. Designed the pedestal for the statue
9 14 17 7

9. President who dedicated the statue
13 2 12 2 13 8 17 5

10. Writer of the statue's inscription
2 4 4 8 13 8   8 3 14 15

HOLIDAYS

1. What holiday is celebrated on February 12?

   _____

2. When is Independence Day?

   _____

3. In what month is Thanksgiving celebrated?

   _____

4. When do we observe Veteran's Day?

   _____

5. What holiday is celebrated on the first Monday in September?

   _____

6. Why do we celebrate Memorial Day?

   _____

7. Which holiday is observed on the second Monday in October?

   _____

8. What famous civil rights activist is honored in January?

   _____

9. On what day is the above activist honored?

   _____

10. On what holiday is a famous parade held in New York City honoring Irish
    ancestry? _____

11. What fairly new holiday is celebrated on the second Sunday in September
    and honors the oldest family members?

    _____

12. What current holiday was originally called Constitution Day?

    _____

46

HOLIDAY WORD FIND

Locate the holidays in the Holiday Box in the word find below. The trick is that the words can be found in any direction. None of them are in a straight line. One has been done for you.

```
L  I  N  D  E  I  N  G  B  A  Y  N  R
J  U  N  C  O  P  E  T  O  D  T  B  O
E  F  S  H  L  W  N  D  E  H  A  D  E
A  Y  A  D  N  S  B  R  T  N  D  L  Y
W  N  O  R  K  R  I  U  L  C  E  D  A
M  E  M  J  I  E  H  T  N  K  M  O  N
E  I  O  G  N  C  O  L  I  T  R  A  M
V  A  R  I  A  S  Q  U  I  G  Y  R  L
E  O  L  M  L  D  A  M  B  U  E  A  S
T  E  R  V  P  Q  L  Y  S  S  D  Y  T
C  O  A  M  W  C  P  G  L  P  R  A  N
G  L  N  K  J  A  F  I  S  P  Y  A  D
N  U  S  D  A  R  V  N  L  Y  I  D  R
I  V  M  K  Y  G  I  G  A  B  L  H  O
T  H  A  N  K  S  P  O  R  A  L  A  B
```

Holiday Box

Lincoln's Birthday   Memorial Day

Martin Luther King, Jr.'s Day   Veteran's Day

Independence Day   Thanksgiving

Columbus Day

THE PLEDGE OF ALLEGIANCE

See how well you know the words and correct spelling to "The Pledge of Allegiance" by filling in the missing words. Then, answer the questions below the pledge. You will need to use reference books.

I pledge _____ to the _____ of the United

_____ of _____ and to the _____

for which it _____, one _____ under

_____, _____, with _____ and

_____ for all.

1. Who wrote the words to the original pledge?_____

2. In what year did children first recite the pledge? _____

3. In what year were the words "under God" added?_____

4. For what special holiday was the pledge written? _____

5. Bellamy's pledge is a bit different from the pledge recited today. What was the original wording to the pledge?

   _____

   _____

   _____

   _____

DATES IN HISTORY

Match each event to its date. Then, find these famous dates in the number search below.

1. Civil War		1917
2. Ratification of the Constitution		1944
3. WWI (U.S. entrance)		1789
4. Discovery of gold in California		1876
5. Declaration of Independence signed		1965
6. First person to walk on the moon		1848
7. Christopher Columbus lands in America		1776
8. Pilgrims land at Plymouth		1812
9. Wright Brothers' flight		1969
10. First American to walk in space		1492
11. Revolutionary War		1620
12. War of 1812		1861
13. First American in space		1775
14. The Alamo (Mexican War)		1903
15. Little Big Horn		1961
16. Battle of the Bulge		1836

```
1  6  2  0  1  6  1  9  4  4
1  0  7  2  9  1  8  4  8  1
3  5  9  1  6  4  6  0  5  3
1  7  8  9  1  8  1  9  7  1
9  9  4  1  3  1  9  0  3  4
6  7  1  7  7  5  2  6  4  9
9  3  1  0  1  8  7  6  8  2
4  5  9  1  3  1  7  7  6  5
1  6  6  1  8  3  6  9  3  7
2  0  5  2  8  6  1  8  1  2
```

FAMOUS FIRSTS

Research to find the answers to these famous firsts.

1. Who was the first president married while in office?

   _____

2. Who was the first president to serve as an official of the Confederate states?

   _____

3. Who was the first American to build a clock?

   _____

4. Who was the first president born a citizen of the United States?

   _____

5. Whose was the first signature to appear on the Declaration of Independence? _____

6. Who was the first president to receive a patent?

   _____

7. Who was the first vice-president to become president automatically?

   _____

8. Who was the first president to be elected?

   _____

9. Which was the first state on the Pacific coast admitted into the Union?

   _____

10. Who was the first president to visit a foreign country while in office?

    _____

11. Who was the first child born to English parents in America?

    _____

12. Which was the first state west of the Mississippi admitted into the Union?

    _____

13. Who was the first American to build a stove for heating?

    _____

14. Who was the first African-American presidential candidate nominated?

    _____

15. Who was the first woman to run for president of the United States?

    _____

GOVERNMENT

1. How many terms can a president serve?_____

2. On which day of the week are national elections held? _____

3. Who is the commander-in-chief of the United States?

   _____

4. Where is the president's office? _____

5. What form of government does the United States have? _____

6. How long is a senator's term in office?_____

7. How often does the United States officially count its people?

   _____

8. Who was America's first Secretary of the Treasury? _____

9. What official is the president of the Senate? _____

10. What are the three branches of the federal government?

    _____

11. What is the highest court in the country? _____

12. How many senators does each state send to Congress? _____

13. What are the United States' two major political parties?

    _____

14. Who was America's first Secretary of State? _____

15. Congress consists of what two groups?

    _____

WARS AND BATTLES

1. During what battle was General George Custer killed?

   _____

2. What was thrown overboard during the Boston Tea Party? _____

3. To whom did General Lee surrender?_____

4. Who is buried at Arlington National Cemetery?_____

5. What Indian chief defeated General Custer? _____

6. What famous patriot warned the people at Lexington that the British were

   coming? _____

7. Who is the commander-in-chief of the Army, Navy, Air Force, and

   Marines? _____

8. During what years did the Civil War take place? _____

9. What do we call a friendly nation in war? _____

10. Who was the commander-in-chief of the Continental Army during the

    Revolutionary War?_____

11. For what primary reason was the Revolutionary War fought?

    _____

12. During what war did Francis Scott Key write "The Star-Spangled Banner"?

    _____

13. In what year did the British capture Washington, D.C.? _____

14. During what war did the colonists fire "the shot heard around the world"?

    _____

15. What American General of the Revolutionary War became the most famous

    traitor in United States history? _____

WHAT DO YOU KNOW?

Fill in the answers to the clues by using the syllables in the box. The number of syllables to be used in each answer is shown in parentheses. The first answer has been done for you.

A	A	A	AR	BRU	CAR	COLN	CON
DE	DY	FE	GIN	VER	HO	DAMS	WASH
ING	I	I	KA	LAN	LAS	LIN	LU
LU	MAD	NO	NON	NIX	O	Y	ON
ROO	SE	SON	TED	TER	GRESS	VELT	VIR
MOUNT	TON						

1. Theodore Roosevelt's nickname   (2)   <u>Teddy</u>

2. The face on the quarter   (3) _____

3. Franklin Roosevelt's middle name   (3) _____

4. The father of the Constitution   (3) _____

5. A month for celebrating presidents   (4) _____

6. President who was the son of a president   (2) _____

7. The capital of Hawaii   (4) _____

8. A president and a peanut farmer   (2) _____

9. The sixteenth president   (2) _____

10. The first president to resign from office   (2) _____

11. An original colony   (4) _____

12. The home of George Washington (2 words)   (3) _____

13. The state closest to Russia   (3) _____

14. A face on Mount Rushmore   (3) _____

15. The Senate and House of Representatives   (2) _____

U.S.A. TRIVIA

1. What song, bearing a nickname used for a soldier, was popular during the Civil War? _____

2. Who wrote "America the Beautiful"? _____

3. Where was the first permanent settlement in the United States?
   _____

4. In what year was gold discovered in California? _____

5. What famous words appear on the Great Seal of the United States?
   _____

6. What does it mean when the American flag is flow at half-mast?
   _____

7. What building is pictured on the back of a penny?
   _____

8. Name the four presidents whose faces are carved in stone on Mount Rushmore. _____

9. Which two states are not in the continental U.S.?
   _____

10. Who was the first president to appear on television?
    _____

11. Which state is often called "The Mother of Presidents"?
    _____

12. Who is the only president never to have married?
    _____

13. During which battle was General George Custer killed?
    _____

14. Which monument in Washington, D.C., is the tallest?
    _____

15. Where did the Wright Brothers make their first flight?
    _____

MORE U.S.A. TRIVIA

1. What president's wife later became an ambassador to the United Nations?

   _____

2. What president's grandson married another president's daughter?

   _____

3. What is America's tallest mountain? _____

4. Where would you find the inscription, "Give me your tired, your poor, your huddled masses yearning to breathe free"?_____

5. What man was the first to fly solo across the Atlantic Ocean?

   _____

6. On what ship did Columbus sail as he traveled to what he thought was the Indies? _____

7. Who was the first to prove that lightning is actually a giant electrical spark?

   _____

8. What man played a naval officer in the movies before becoming president?

   _____

9. What astronaut minded *Apollo II* while Armstrong and Aldrin made history? _____

10. Who invented peanut butter? _____

11. What president's wife made ice cream popular in the United States?

    _____

12. Who designed the White House?_____

13. How many members are in Congress? _____

14. What American man was an auto industry pioneer?

    _____

15. What state consists of a group of islands in the Pacific Ocean?

    _____

THREE OF A KIND

Next to each heading, name three or more U.S. names or dates that belong. Be prepared to explain your answers.

1. Presidents' first names_____

2. Mountain ranges _____

3. Inventors _____

4. Astronauts _____

5. Famous women _____

6. Monuments _____

7. Presidents on currency_____

8. Presidents' spouses _____

9. Capital cities _____

10. States ending with "a"_____

11. Original thirteen colonies _____

12. Signers of the Declaration of Independence _____

13. Important dates in history _____

14. Presidents' nicknames _____

15. Holidays_____

16. Birth states of presidents _____

17. State flowers _____

18. Famous military personnel _____

19. Landmarks_____

20. Natural wonders _____

56

NUMBERS

1. How old must one be to be the president of the U.S.? _____

2. How many terms may the president serve? _____

3. How tall is the Statue of Liberty? _____

4. How many uses for the peanut did George Washington Carver discover?
   _____

5. How many presidents have held office in the U.S.? _____

6. How long is a senator's term in office? _____

7. How many branches are there in the federal government? _____

8. How many senators does each state send to Congress? _____

9. How many rooms are there in the White House? _____

10. How many people were aboard the *Mayflower*? _____

11. How many colors are on the U.S. flag? _____

12. How many states make up the U.S.? _____

13. How many original colonies were there? _____

14. How long was William Henry Harrison's term of office? _____

15. How many words are in the Gettysburg Address? _____

16. How many presidents were there in the 1980s? _____

17. How old must a citizen be to vote in the U.S.? _____

18. How many oceans border the U.S.? _____

19. How many stripes are on the U.S. flag? _____

20. How many presidents were never elected to the presidency or to the
    vice-presidency? _____

SECRET MESSAGE

Answer each question below. Then, fill in the code with the correct letters to find out this famous quote.

1. If Lincoln was President before Cleveland, circle D. If not, circle T.

2. If the Statue of Liberty was given to the U.S. by England, circle E. If not, circle B.

3. If Washington lived in the White House, circle L. If not, circle H.

4. If Kennedy's face is on the half-dollar, circle V. If not, circle S.

5. If Robert E. Lee was a Union general, circle A. If not, circle Y.

6. If Kansas is east of the Rockies, circle O. If not, circle I.

7. If Grover Cleveland was the 22nd and 24th president, circle A. If not, circle P.

8. If Miss Liberty is holding the book of laws in her left hand, circle M. If not, circle N.

9. If Houston is the capital of Texas, circle L. If not, circle G.

10. If Betsy Ross is said to have made the U.S. flag, circle L. If not, circle M.

11. If Eisenhower's nickname was Ike, circle E. If not, circle T.

12. If there are 103 rooms in the White House, circle T. If not, circle R.

13. If there are more red stripes than white stripes on the U.S. flag, circle T. If not, circle S.

14. If Ben Franklin's face is on Mt. Rushmore, circle L. If not, circle I.

```
 __  __  __  __      __  __      __  __  __  __  __  __  __
 9  14   4  11       8  11      10  14  2  11  12  13   5

 __  __      __  __  __  __      __  __      __  __  __  __  __
 6  12       9  14   4  11       8  11       1  11  17  13   3
```

58

CODES

Each group of words below is a list of related words in code. Each group has its own code. Brainstorm some words to fit each category. Then, see whether any of your brainstormed words match the coded words. When you have identified a word, use the known letters to help decode other words within the group.

Presidents

ex. Ford

L G O L _____

H G E R A S J L D S _____

T M G J G S _____

P A S K D P S _____

F K V A S P M N _____

M A E M S R D H M T _____

K P M I M P G S B _____

C M O O M T E D S _____

G B G F E _____

K G T L M T _____

National Symbols

ex. Uncle Sam

A K P W H K G B D H _____

D W O T D O Z Q D W T P M H D _____

V O Z Q H O L Z H _____

D W O W B H G N Z P V H T W I _____

Z P V H T W I V H Z Z _____

D W O W B H G N N T H H Q G S _____

U G X D W P W B W P G X _____

L H W W I D V B T L O Q Q T H D D _____

S G B X W T B D K S G T H _____

UNITED STATES OF AMERICA

There are over 100 words that can be made from the letters in "United States of America." How many can you find?

_____   _____   _____
_____   _____   _____
_____   _____   _____
_____   _____   _____
_____   _____   _____
_____   _____   _____
_____   _____   _____
_____   _____   _____
_____   _____   _____
_____   _____   _____
_____   _____   _____
_____   _____   _____
_____   _____   _____
_____   _____   _____
_____   _____   _____
_____   _____   _____
_____   _____   _____
_____   _____   _____

TRIVIA I

1. "We the People of the United States" are the first six words to what important document?_____

2. Who was the first American to walk on the moon?

   _____

3. Who were the only two Americans to appear on a U.S. coin who were not presidents? _____

4. What is the only state that borders only one other state?_____

5. How are the fifty stars on the U.S. flag arranged? _____

   _____

6. What were the two capital cities before Washington, D.C.?

   _____

7. How tall is the Washington Memorial?_____

8. Who wrote "The Star-Spangled Banner"? _____

9. In which hand does Miss Liberty hold her torch? _____

10. In what state would Washington, D.C., be found?

    _____

11. What do we call a government in which the people elect their leaders?

    _____

12. What famous words appear on the Great Seal of the United States?

    _____

13. What is the only "island" state that is not an island?

    _____

14. Who built the first airplane? _____

15. Who killed President Lincoln? _____

TRIVIA II

1. On which coin is Jefferson's home pictured?

   _____

2. On the dollar bill, is Washington facing to the right or to the left?

   _____

3. Of all the states, how many state names are made of only one syllable?

   _____

4. Whose face is on the half-dollar? _____

5. Which president's wife was called "Lemonade Lucy"? _____

6. Which president was born on the 4th of July? _____

7. Who was the author of *Poor Richard's Almanac*? _____

8. Who was the United States named after? _____

9. Who was the first person to sign The Declaration of Independence?

   _____

10. Who was the founder of the American Red Cross?

    _____

11. In which state is Plymouth Rock located? _____

12. Who discovered over 200 uses for the peanut?_____

13. What is the longest river in the United States?_____

14. Which state is called "The Presidents' State"? _____

15. What are the seven basic colors used on most national flags?

    _____

THE STATUE OF LIBERTY

There are over 125 words that can be made from the letters in "The Statue of Liberty." How many can you find?

_____   _____   _____

_____   _____   _____

_____   _____   _____

_____   _____   _____

_____   _____   _____

_____   _____   _____

_____   _____   _____

_____   _____   _____

_____   _____   _____

_____   _____   _____

_____   _____   _____

_____   _____   _____

_____   _____   _____

_____   _____   _____

_____   _____   _____

_____   _____   _____

_____   _____   _____

_____   _____   _____

_____   _____   _____

CLASSIFYING

For each set of four, find something that they have in common. Some are easy to see, but others are rather difficult and are going to need research to find. (Note: Do not use the following responses as answers: *presidents*, *people*, *states*, and *cities*.)

1. Roosevelt, Lincoln, Jefferson, and Washington _____

2. Carter, Garfield, Buchanan, and Polk _____

3. Washington, Jefferson, Madison, and Monroe _____

4. Delaware, Georgia, Massachusetts, and Pennsylvania

_____

5. Illinois, Indiana, West Virginia, and Ohio _____

6. Alabama, Florida, Georgia, and Indiana

_____

7. North Dakota, South Dakota, Montana, and Washington

_____

8. Massachusetts, Missouri, Mississippi, and Michigan _____

9. Carson City, Oklahoma City, Salt Lake City, and Jefferson City

_____

10. Jackson, Jefferson City, Lincoln, and Madison

_____

11. Illinois, Missouri, Massachusetts, and Arizona

_____

12. Kennedy, Washington, Lincoln, and Roosevelt

_____

13. Wright, Franklin, Bell, and Edison _____

14. Lincoln, Garfield, McKinley, and Kennedy

_____

15. Lincoln, Grant, Reagan, and Ford _____

Teacher Note: See the answer key on page 80 for an alternate activity.

EQUATIONS

Each equation below contains the initials of words that will make it complete. Find the missing words. The first one is done for you.

1. 132 = R in the WH ____Rooms in the White House____

2. 103 = P aboard the M _____

3. 50 = S in the US _____

4. 272 = W in the GA _____

5. 42 = P of the US* _____

6. 535 = M of C _____

7. 4 = F on MR _____

8. 56 = S on the D of I _____

9. 551 = H of the S of L _____

10. 10 = A in the B of R _____

11. 13 = S on the USF _____

12. 3 = C on the USF _____

13. 3 = PM in WDC _____

14. 6 = Y of a S T of O _____

15. 1 = P of the US _____

*Teacher Note: Be sure to adjust this number for your current year.

CATEGORIES

For each of the following categories, fill in the names of items that belong. Use each letter of the category for an item within it. Some of the first category has been done for you.

T
a
y
l
o
r
i
e
r
c
e

PRESIDENTS

LANDMARKS

INVENTORS

STATES

CAPITALS

FAMOUS PEOPLE

66

SECRET MESSAGE

Answer each question below. Then, fill in the code with the correct letter to find the famous quote from Will Rogers.

"

— —————   ———   —
7   10 5 4 5 9   2 5 8   6

                                                    "
———   —   —————   —— ——.
2 6 10   7   1 7 1 10 8   11 7 3 5

1. If the Statue of Liberty was a gift from France, circle D. If it was from England, circle N.

2. If the Atlantic Ocean is west of the United States, circle A. If it is east, circle M.

3. If Francis Bellamy wrote the words to "The Pledge of Allegiance," circle K. If Lincoln wrote those famous words, circle E.

4. If John Kennedy was our 35th president, circle V. If Nixon was, circle E.

5. If Kennedy is pictured on the two-dollar bill, circle L. If Jefferson is, circle E.

6. If the French burned the White House, circle F. If the British did, circle A.

7. If George Washington Carver invented peanut butter, circle I. If Edison did, circle F.

8. If Jefferson City is the capital of Mississippi, circle J. If it is Missouri's capital, circle T.

9. If John Adams was the first vice-president, circle R. If it was Thomas Jefferson, circle N.

10. If Washington's home is Monticello, circle L. If it is Mt. Vernon, circle N.

11. If Roosevelt was elected for two nonconsecutive terms, circle R. If Cleveland was, circle L.

TRUE OR FALSE

Are the following true or false? Write *true* or *false* in the blank before each. After each false statement, write the word or words that will make it true.

1. _____ The Pacific Ocean is east of the United States.

2. _____ The Statue of Liberty was given to the United States by England.

3. _____ Robert E. Lee was a Confederate general in the Civil War.

4. _____ Canada is a state in the United States.

5. _____ America was named after Amerigo Vespucci.

6. _____ Ronald Reagan was once a movie star.

7. _____ The capital of Delaware if Denver.

8. _____ Ben Franklin helped write the Declaration of Independence.

9. _____ John F. Kennedy was a Republican president.

10. _____ The Statue of Liberty holds a tablet in her right hand.

11. _____ Mt. Everest is the tallest mountain in the United States.

12. _____ The flag flying at half-mast represents a time of mourning.

13. _____ Grover Cleveland was the 22nd and 24th president of the United States.

14. _____ John F. Kennedy's middle name was Frederick.

15. _____ Washington, D.C. is located in Maryland.

WHICH IS IT?

Circle the name or number on the right that matches the words on the left.

1.	State in the U.S.	Los Angeles	Italy	Florida
2.	Thomas Jefferson	3rd president	16th president	25th president
3.	States in the U.S.	13	8	50
4.	Rooms in the White House	206	132	102
5.	Capital of Illinois	Springfield	Austin	Dover
6.	16th president	Adams	Carter	Lincoln
7.	American river	Nile	Amazon	Mississippi
8.	People aboard the *Mayflower*	132	103	272
9.	Great lake that lies entirely within the U.S.	Huron	Michigan	Superior
10.	Amendments in the Bill of Rights	10	11	12
11.	Presidents before Eisenhower	35	33	30
12.	Face on Mt. Rushmore	Roosevelt	Kennedy	Adams
13.	An original colony	Illinois	Pennsylvania	Ohio
14.	Pictured on a U.S. coin	Nixon	Adams	Lincoln
15.	Republican president	Carter	Ford	Kennedy

SIX-LETTER WORDS

In each of the squares below is the first or second half of a six-letter word or name related to the United States. Can you match these halves to form 22 words? The first has been done for you.

MON	DEN	ART	AII	REA	DGE
STA	CAR	SEN	MAN	GON	TRU
SON	STA	HAW	TUE	LOR	SKA
TUB	ROE	BAR	VER	TED	WIL
ALA	ORE	GAN	ATE	HOO	TON
TAY	BOS	TES	TON	KAN	HUR
SAS	MAN	TER	NEV	UNI	ADA
VER	PLE				

1.   Monroe _____
2. _____
3. _____
4. _____
5. _____
6. _____
7. _____
8. _____
9. _____
10. _____
11. _____
12. _____

13. _____
14. _____
15. _____
16. _____
17. _____
18. _____
19. _____
20. _____
21. _____
22. _____

IS IT TRUE OR FALSE?

Are the following true or false? Write true or false in the blank before each. After each false statement, write the word or words that will make it true.

1. _____ Jamestown, Virginia, was the first permanent settlement in the United States. _____

2. _____ George Washington was called "The Father of the Constitution." _____

3. _____ Clara Barton made the first United States flag.

_____

4. _____ There are 132 rooms in the White House. _____

5. _____ There are more white than red stripes on the U.S. flag.

_____

6. _____ Abraham Lincoln was assassinated in Ford's Theatre. _____

7. _____ John F. Kennedy and William Taft are the only two presidents buried in Arlington National Cemetery. _____

8. _____ Abraham Lincoln is pictured on the two-dollar bill. _____

9. _____ The second and sixth presidents were father and son. _____

10. _____ John Glenn was the first man in space. _____

11. _____ Richard Nixon was the first president to talk to a man on the moon. _____

12. _____ The teddy bear was named after Theodore Roosevelt.

_____

13. _____ The Revolutionary War began in 1861. _____

14. _____ The first president to reside in the White House was John Adams. _____

15. _____ The first president to receive a patent was Thomas Jefferson. _____

THE NAME GAME

To the Teacher: Divide the students into groups of four. Duplicate pages 72–74, one set per group. Cut each page into fours, separating the lists. Have each student draw three lists from the group's stack of twelve. One at a time, each student will attempt, in three minutes, to get the others in the group to name the things on a list by giving only clues (and not saying the words).

1. North America	1. Washington, D.C.
2. Bald eagle	2. 1492
3. 1776	3. Congress
4. George Washington	4. Thomas Jefferson
5. Mt. Rushmore	5. Lake Michigan
6. Declaration of Independence	6. Bill of Rights
7. *Mayflower*	7. Martin Luther King, Jr.
8. The Alamo	8. Thomas Edison
9. Legislative branch	9. Civil War
10. Benjamin Franklin	10. Fifty states

1. 1620	1. Vice-president
2. "In God We Trust"	2. Stars and Stripes
3. Judicial branch	3. Old Faithful
4. Theodore Roosevelt	4. Abraham Lincoln
5. The White House	5. Fourth of July
6. New York City	6. Jefferson Memorial
7. "Star-Spangled Banner"	7. U.S. Constitution
8. Gettysburg Address	8. The Senate
9. Delaware	9. Statue of Liberty
10. Henry Ford	10. Mt. Vernon

THE NAME GAME (CONT.)

1. John Glenn
2. Quakers
3. Niagara Falls
4. Richard Nixon
5. *The Santa Maria*
6. Jamestown
7. Christopher Columbus
8. Hawaii
9. Republican
10. Tallahassee

1. Mississippi River
2. Christa McAuliffe
3. The Wall (or the Vietnam Memorial)
4. Cesar Chavez
5. Pilgrims
6. Illinois
7. Sacramento
8. Arlington National Cemetery
9. The *Pinta*
10. Virginia Dare

1. Baton Rouge
2. 1848
3. John Adams
4. Sacajawea
5. George Washington Carver
6. Nevada
7. Potomac River
8. Harriet Tubman
9. Frederick Douglass
10. Ford's Theatre

1. James Madison
2. Tomb of the Unknown Solider
3. Lewis and Clark
4. John Hancock
5. Alaska
6. 1969
7. Dover
8. Democrat
9. Peary and Henson
10. The Senate

THE NAME GAME (CONT.)

1. Amerigo Vespucci
2. Emma Lazarus
3. Henry Hudson
4. Lake Michigan
5. Mt. McKinley
6. Appalachian Mountains
7. Charles Lindbergh
8. The *Nina*
9. Thanksgiving
10. Gateway Arch

1. Neil Armstrong
2. Paul Revere
3. Bill Cosby
4. Emily Dickinson
5. Colorado River
6. Old Faithful
7. Wright Brothers
8. WWI
9. Pearl Harbor
10. Empire State Building

1. Sally Ride
2. Liberty Bell
3. Pocahantas
4. Rocky Mountains
5. Arlington Cemetary
6. Amelia Earhart
7. Samuel Morse
8. Seattle
9. Sears Tower
10. Chief Joseph

1. Pocahontas
2. Pacific Ocean
3. Miles Standish
4. Bill Clinton
5. Mt. St. Helens
6. Francis Scott Key
7. Zachary Taylor
8. Benedict Arnold
9. Kristi Yamaguchi
10. Washington Monument

ANSWER KEY

Page 3
1. Abraham Lincoln
2. James Madison
3. John Adams
4. Thomas Jefferson
5. Grover Cleveland
6. Zachary Taylor
7. Abraham Lincoln
8. John Kennedy and William Taft
9. Franklin D. Roosevelt
10. James Madison
11. Benjamin Harrison
12. James Madison
13. James Buchanan
14. Richard Nixon
15. John Garfield, Harry Truman, Gerald Ford, George Bush and Bill Clinton

Page 4
1. John Qunicy Adams
2. Theodore Roosevelt
3. John Tyler
4. Andrew Jackson
5. George Washington
6. Ronald Reagan
7. John Adams
8. Thomas Jefferson
9. Franklin Roosevelt
10. Gerald Ford
11. Abraham Lincoln
12. Thomas
13. Ulysses Grant
14. Richard Nixon
15. William Harrison

Page 5
1. Truman
2. Polk
3. Madison
4. Fillmore
5. Garfield
6. Taylor
7. Washington
8. Jackson
9. Coolidge
10. Hoover

Page 6
Across
1. Washington
2. Nixon
3. Eisenhower
4. Ford
5. Adams
6. Monroe
7. Bush
8. Kennedy
9. Grant
Down
1. Lincoln
2. Taft
3. Jefferson
4. Filmore

5. Roosevelt
6. Wilson
7. Cleveland
8. Madison
9. Reagan

Page 7
1. John
2. Dwight
3. Ronald
4. Thomas
5. Richard
6. Abraham
7. Jimmy
8. Herbert
9. Theodore or Franklin
10. George
11. Calvin
12. Grover
13. Ulysses
14. Zachary
15. William
16. Harry
17. James
18. James
19. James
20. Lyndon

Page 8
1. Dwight Eisenhower
2. William Clinton
3. Gerald Ford
4. Martin Van Buren
5. Ronald Reagan
6. Calvin Coolidge
7. George Washington
8. Franklin Pierce
9. Benjamin Harrison
10. Abraham Lincoln
11. George Bush
12. Ulysses Grant
13. Richard Nixon
14. Teddy Roosevelt
15. James Madison

Page 9
These answers on page 9 and 10 stand for 1995. After 1995, some answers may vary.
1. 67; 2. 91; 3. 83; 4. 85; 5. 73; 6. 81; 7. 78; 8. 80; 9. 68; 10. 72; 11. 54; 12. 66; 13. 74; 14. 65; 15. 77; 16. 56; 17. 67; 18. 63; 19. 71; 20. 50; 21. 56; 22. 71; 23. 68; 24. 71; 25. 58; 26. 61; 27. 73; 28. 68; 29. 58; 30. 61; 31. 90; 32. 63; 33. 88; 34. 79; 35. 46; 36. 65; 37. 81

Page 10
1. See page 9.
2. Adams and Jefferson
3. Franklin Roosevelt
4. October
5. Ronald Reagan

6. 19
7. 5
8. Adams and Jackson
9. New Jersey
10. 8
11. Kennedy
12. 4/23/1791
13. 8
14. 16

Page 11
1. Ike
2. Father of the Declaration of Independence
3. F.D.R.
4. Old Tippecanoe
5. Honest Abe
6. Father of His Country
7. Old Hickory
8. Old Rough and Ready
9. Tricky Dick
10. Rough Rider
11. Father of the Constitution
12. Big Bill
13. Accidental President
14. The Dark Horse
15. Give 'Em Hell Harry

Page 12

Page 13
1. George Washington
2. Calvin Coolidge
3. Thomas Jefferson
4. Dwight Eisenhower
5. William Taft
6. Lyndon Johnson
7. Grover Cleveland
8. Franklin Roosevelt
9. Theodore Roosevelt
10. Richard Nixon
11. William Harrison
12. William Taft
13. George Washington
14. John Tyler
15. Abraham Lincoln

ANSWER KEY (CONT.)

Page 14
1. Harry Truman
2. Martin Luther King
3. Patrick Henry
4. Will Rogers
5. Francis Scott Key
6. Alexander Graham Bell
7. Neil Armstrong
8. Neil Armstrong
9. Franklin Roosevelt
10. John Kennedy
11. Ben Franklin
12. John Paul Jones
13. Abraham Lincoln
14. General Douglas MacArthur
15. Abraham Lincoln

Page 15
1. Christopher Columbus
2. Neil Armstrong
3. Magellan
4. Alan Shepard
5. the Pilgrims
6. John Glenn
7. Sally Ride
8. Amerigo Vespucci
9. Lewis and Clark
10. Christa McAuliffe
11. Cartier
12. Peary and Henson
13. Sacajawea
14. Joliet and Marquette
15. Leif Ericson

Page 16
Benjamin Franklin

Page 17
1. I
2. C
3. B
4. L
5. K
6. E
7. H
8. M
9. G
10. O
11. A
12. F
13. D
14. N
15. J

Page 18
1. Taft
2. Polk
3. Grant
4. Bush
5. Carter
6. Ford
7: Hayes
8. Bell
9. Clark
10. Morse
11. Keller

Page 19
1. Adams
2. Ford
3. Madison
4. Garfield
5. Jefferson
6. Eisenhower
7. Armstrong
8. Vespucci
9. Edison
10. Earhart

Page 20
1. Ben Franklin
2. Johnny Appleseed
3. Francis Key
4. Daniel Boone
5. Ernest Hemingway
6. Jefferson Davis
7. P.T. Barnum
8. Jackie Robinson
9. Betsy Ross
10. Jim Thorpe
11. Sitting Bull
12. Clara Barton
13. Louisa May Alcott
14. George Carver
15. Susan B. Anthony

Page 21
1. first successful airplane
2. telephone
3. cotton gin
4. bifocal glasses
5. assembly-line method of production
6. polio vaccine
7. steel plow
8. vulcanization of rubber
9. sewing machine
10. Kodak® camera
11. steamboat
12. phonograph
13. quick-freezing process
14. electric telegraph
15. railroad sleeping car
16. 200 uses of the peanut

Page 22
1. Potomac
2. 1791
3. Pierre L'Enfant
4. 1800
5. the Senate and the House of Representatives
6. the White House
7. no
8. "We, the people of the United States"
9. the security of the nation
10. President Kennedy, President Taft, and thousands of people who served in our armed forces
11. unknown soldiers who died while serving our country (Three are buried

within the tomb.)
12. the Smithsonian
13. paper money and stamps
14. Washington, Lincoln, and Jefferson
15. John Adams

Page 23
1. Illinois
2. South Carolina
3. Hawaii
4. Virginia
5. Alabama
6. West Virginia
7. Massachusetts
8. Connecticut
9. New York
10. Arizona
11. New Mexico
12. Oklahoma
13. Alaska
14. Minnesota
15. Vermont
16. Delaware
17. Texas
18. Maine
19. Montana
20. Iowa
21. North Dakota
22. Arkansas
23. Pennsylvania
24. Nevada
25. Kentucky

Page 24
1. California
2. New Jersey
3. Louisianna
4. Oregon
5. Florida
6. Michigan
7. Ohio
8. Indiana
9. Nebraska
10. Colorado
11. Kansas
12. South Dakota
13. Mississippi
14. New Hampshire
15. Rhode Island
16. Georgia
17. Utah
18. Wisconsin
19. North Carolina
20. Washington
21. Tennessee
22. Idaho
23. Missouri
24. Wyoming
25. Maryland

Pages 25–26
1. Hawaii
2. Kentucky
3. West Virginia
4. Colorado
5. Illinois
6. Wyoming
7. Massachusetts
8. New Hampshire
9. Washington
10. Alabama
11. Rhode Island
12. Utah
13. South Dakota
14. Connecticut
15. Nebraska
16. California
17. Missouri
18. Georgia
19. Maine
20. Texas
21. Maryland
22. Alaska
23. New Mexico
24. Kansas
25. Mississippi
26. Arkansas
27. North Carolina
28. South Carolina
29. Florida
30. Virginia
31. Indiana
32. Pennsylvania
33. Nevada
34. New Jersey
35. Arizona
36. Minnesota
37. Oklahoma
38. Iowa
39. Ohio
40. Delaware
41. Tennessee
42. Montana
43. Vermont
44. Wisconsin
45. Idaho
46. New York
47. Oregon
48. Louisiana
49. North Dakota
50. Michigan

ANSWER KEY (CONT.)

Page 27
1. North Carolina or South Carolina
2. Honolulu
3. Jefferson City
4. Indiana or Indianapolis
5. Texas
6. St. Paul
7. Kentucky
8. Hartford
9. Helena
10. Jackson
11. Richmond
12. Idaho
13. Trenton
14. Frankfort
15. California
16. Juneau
17. St. Louis
18. Maryland
19. Delaware
20. Charleston
21. Kentucky
22. Annapolis

Page 28

Page 29
Answers can be in any order.
Michigan
Kentucky
Nebraska
Alaska
Washington
Idaho
Maryland
Delaware
Oregon
Florida
Ohio
Arkansas
Tennessee
Montana
Virginia

Page 30
1. Alaska
2. Arizona
3. Delaware
4. Hawaii
5. Kansas
6. Maine
7. Michigan
8. New York
9. North Carolina
10. Pennsylvania
11. Rhode Island
12. Virginia
13. Washington
14. Hawaii
15. Alaska

Page 31

Pages 32–35
1. Alaska
2. Oregon
3. New York
4. Connecticut
5. Idaho
6. North Dakota
7. Indiana
8. Utah
9. Arkansas
10. Iowa
11. Kentucky
12. Vermont
13. Pennsylvania
14. Oklahoma
15. South Dakota
16. Louisiana
17. Kansas
18. Wisconsin
19. Rhode Island
20. Ohio
21. North Carolina
22. California
23. Maryland
24. New Mexico
25. Virginia
26. Hawaii
27. Tennessee
28. Missouri
29. Nevada
30. Alabama
31. Michigan
32. New Jersey
33. South Carolina
34. West Virginia
35. Wyoming
36. Arizona
37. Montana
38. Minnesota
39. Washington
40. Texas
41. Florida
42. Georgia
43. Massachusetts
44. Nebraska
45. Illinois
46. New Hampshire
47. Delaware
48. Maine
49. Colorado
50. Mississippi

Page 36
1. copper
2. France
3. Liberty Island
4. in friendship and in honor of mutual belief in liberty
5. a torch
6. a book of laws
7. a crown with huge spikes
8. 151' 1"
9. Bartholdi
10. Grover Cleveland
11. Answer will vary according to the current year.
12. October 28, 1886
13. Liberty Enlightening the World
14. 450,000 lbs.
15. Richard M. Hunt
16. the seven continents and the seven seas
17. Emma Lazarus
18. immigrants

Page 37
The Statue of Liberty

Page 38
1. The Statue of Freedom
2. The Statue of Liberty
3. Jefferson Memorial
4. Jefferson, Lincoln, and Washington
5. St. Louis, Missouri
6. Arlington National Cemetery, Arlington, VA
7. the military might of the U.S.
8. Washington Monument
9. north of Arlington National Cemetery in Washington D.C.
10. servicemen raising the American flag on Iwo Jima during WWII
11. Vietnam Veterans Memorial (The Wall)
12. Philadelphia

Page 39
1. red, white, and blue
2. Old Glory or the Stars and Stripes
3. Betsy Ross
4. thirteen
5. seven; six
6. thirteen
7. hardiness and courage
8. the fifty states
9. as a signal of mourning
10. purity and innocence
11. the president is not in Washington D.C.
12. in 1969 (by Neil Armstrong and Edwin Aldrin)
13. five rows of six stars and four rows of five stars
14. vigilance, perseverance, and justice
15. It must be burned.

Page 40
1. the second
2. John Adams
3. 1600 Pennsylvania Avenue
4. James Hoban
5. in the west wing
6. The British burned the building.
7. 132
8. the President's House and the Executive Mansion
9. no
10. red, green, and blue
11. Abraham Lincoln
12. 1792
13. James Madison
14. Theodore Roosevelt

Page 41
1. South Dakota
2. Montana
3. Massachusetts
4. Washington
5. Florida
6. Texas
7. Alaska
8. Wyoming
9. New Mexico
10. Hawaii
11. Arizona
12. Wyoming
13. Arizona
14. South Dakota
15. New York
16. Wyoming
17. California

Page 42
1. Mississippi
2. Russia
3. New York City (in 1995)
4. Washington, D.C.
5. North America
6. Pacific Ocean
7. Alaska
8. Canada
9. Mt. McKinley
10. Alaska and Hawaii
11. Atlantic Ocean
12. Mexico
13. Maine
14. Rocky Mountains and Appalachian Mountains
15. Arizona

Page 43
1. Mt. McKinley, Alaska
2. Mt. St. Elias, Alaska
3. Foraker, Alaska
4. Blackburn, Alaska
5. Bona, Alaska
6. Sanford, Alaska
7. Chugach Mountains, Alaska
8. Mt. Whitney, California
9. Mt. Elbert, Colorado
10. Mt. Rainier, Washington
11. Evans, Colorado
12. Longs Peak, Colorado
13. Mount Shasta, California
14. Pike's Peak, Colorado
15. Mount Wrangell, Alaska
16. Mauna Kea, Hawaii
17. Mauna Loa, Hawaii

Page 44
1. Orlando
2. Washington, D.C.
3. San Francisco
4. Hawaii
5. Massachusetts
6. Chicago
7. Texas
8. St. Louis
9. Philadelphia
10. New York City
11. Seattle
12. South Dakota
13. Alaska
14. New York City
15. Houston

Page 45
"Give me your tired, your poor, your huddled masses yearning to breathe free."
1. New York Harbor
2. Bartholdi
3. France
4. green
5. right
6. Liberty Island
7. copper
8. Hunt
9. Cleveland
10. Emma Lazarus

Page 46
1. Lincoln's Birthday
2. July 4
3. November
4. November 11
5. Labor Day
6. to honor Americans who gave their lives for their country
7. Columbus Day
8. Martin Luther King, Jr.
9. January 15
10. St. Patrick's Day
11. Grandparents' Day
12. Citizenship Day

Page 47

Page 48
allegiance, flag, States, America, Republic, stands, Nation, God, indivisible, liberty, justice
1. Francis Bellamy
2. 1892
3. 1954
4. Columbus Day (the 400th anniversary of Columbus' arrival)
5. "I pledge allegiance to my flag and to the Republic for which it stands – one Nation indivisible – with liberty and juctice for all."

Page 49
1. 1861
2. 1789
3. 1917
4. 1848
5. 1776
6. 1969
7. 1492
8. 1620
9. 1903
10. 1965
11. 1775
12. 1812
13. 1961
14. 1836
15. 1876
16. 1944

78

ANSWER KEY (CONT.)

Page 50
1. Grover Cleveland
2. John Tyler
3. Benjamin Banneker
4. Martin Van Buren
5. John Hancock
6. Abraham Lincoln
7. John Tyler
8. George Washington
9. California
10. Theodore Roosevelt
11. Virginia Dare
12. Missouri
13. Benjamin Franklin
14. Frederick Douglas
15. Victoria Woodhull

Page 51
1. two
2. Tuesday
3. the president
4. in the White House (west wing)
5. a republic or democracy
6. six years
7. every ten years
8. Alexander Hamilton
9. the vice-president
10. Executive, Legislative, and Judicial
11. the Supreme Court
12. two
13. Republican and Democrat
14. Thomas Jefferson
15. The Senate and the House of Representatives

Page 52
1. the Battle of Little Big Horn
2. tea
3. General Ulysses S. Grant
4. Presidents Kennedy and Taft and thousands of people who served in the U.S. armed services
5. Sitting Bull
6. Paul Revere
7. The President of the United States
8. 1861–1865
9. an ally
10. George Washington
11. to gain independence from Great Britain
12. the War of 1812
13. 1814
14. Revolutionary War (at Concord)
15. Benedict Arnold

Page 53
1. Teddy
2. Washington
3. Delano
4. Madison
5. February
6. Adams
7. Honolulu
8. Carter
9. Lincoln
10. Nixon
11. Virginia

12. Mount Vernon
13. Alaska
14. Roosevelt (Theodore)
15. Congress

Page 54
1. "When Johnny Comes Marching Home"
2. Katherine L. Bates
3. Jamestown, Virginia
4. 1848
5. *E Pluribus Unum*
6. symbol of mourning
7. the Lincoln Memorial
8. Washington, Lincoln, Roosevelt, and Jefferson
9. Alaska and Hawaii
10. Franklin Roosevelt
11. Virginia
12. James Buchanan
13. the Battle of Little Big Horn
14. the Washington Memorial
15. Kitty Hawk, North Carolina

Page 55
1. Eleanor Roosevelt
2. Dwight D. Eisenhower (David to Julie Nixon)
3. Mt. McKinley
4. at the base of the Statue of Liberty
5. Charles Lindbergh
6. *Santa Maria*
7. Benjamin Franklin
8. Ronald Reagan
9. Mike Collins
10. George Washington Carver
11. Dolly Madison
12. James Hoban
13. 535
14. Henry Ford
15. Hawaii

Page 56
Answers will vary.

Page 57
1. 35
2. 2
3. 151' 1"
4. 200
5. Answers will vary depending on the current year.
6. 6 years
7. 3
8. 2
9. 132
10. 103
11. 3
12. 50
13. 13
14. 1 month
15. 272
16. 3
17. 18
18. 2
19. 13
20. 1

Page 58
1. D
2. B
3. H
4. V
5. Y
6. O
7. A
8. M
9. G
10. L
11. E
12. R
13. T
14. I
"Give me liberty or give me death."

Page 59
Presidents
Taft
Washington
Reagan
Lincoln
McKinley
Eisenhower
Cleveland
Jefferson
Adams
Carter
National Symbols
White House
Stars and Stripes
bald eagle
Statue of Liberty
Liberty Bell
Statue of Freedom
Constitution
Gettysburg Address
Mount Rushmore

Page 60
Answers will vary from student to student. Together, the students can make a master list.

Page 61
1. The Constitution
2. Neil Armstrong
3. Ben Franklin and Susan B. Anthony
4. Maine
5. 5 rows of 6 stars and 4 rows of 5 stars
6. New York City and Philadelphia
7. 555 feet
8. Francis Scott Key
9. her right
10. none (It is a district.)
11. a republic or a democracy
12. *E Pluribus Unum*
13. Rhode Island
14. Samuel Langley
15. John Wilkes Booth

ANSWER KEY (CONT.)

Page 62
1. nickel
2. right
3. one (Maine)
4. John F. Kennedy
5. Rutherford B. Hayes
6. Calvin Coolidge
7. Benjamin Franklin
8. Amerigo Vespucci
9. John Hancock
10. Clara Barton
11. Massachusetts
12. George Washington Carver
13. the Mississippi River
14. Virginia
15. red, white, green, blue, yellow, black, and orange

Page 63
Answers will vary from student to student. Together, the students can make a master list.

Page 64
To simplify this activity, rearrange the order of the following answers and give them to the students. Have them do a matching activity with the answers instead of finding them from scratch.
1. on Mt. Rushmore
2. first name of James
3. from Virginia
4. original colonies
5. cardinal as state bird
6. end in "A" and/or have seven letters
7. joined the Union in 1889
8. begin with "M"
9. capital cities whose names end in "city"
10. capitals named for presidents
11. name originated from an Indian tribe or language
12. all presidents on U.S. coins
13. inventors
14. presidents who have been assassinated
15. Republican presidents

Page 65
1. rooms in the White House
2. people aboard the *Mayflower*
3. states in the United States
4. words in the Gettysburg Address
5. presidents of the United States
6. members of Congress
7. faces on Mt. Rushmore
8. signatures on the Declaration of Independence
9. height of the Statue of Liberty
10. Amendments in the Bill of Rights
11. stripes on the United States flag
12. colors on the United States flag
13. presidential memorials in Washington, D.C.
14. years of a Senator's term in office
15. president of the United States

Page 66
Answers will vary.

Page 67
"I never met a man I didn't like."
1. D
2. M
3. K
4. V
5. E
6. A
7. I
8. T
9. R
10. N
11. L

Page 68
1. false (west)
2. false (France)
3. true
4. false (a country in North America)
5. true
6. true
7. false (Dover)
8. true
9. false (Democrat)
10. false (left)
11. false (Mt. McKinley)
12. true
13. true
14. false (Fitzgerald)
15. false (not in a state; is a district)

Page 69
1. Florida
2. 3rd
3. 50
4. 132
5. Springfield
6. Lincoln
7. Mississippi
8. 103
9. Michigan
10. 10
11. 33
12. Roosevelt
13. Pennsylvania
14. Lincoln
15. Ford

Page 70
Answers will be in no particular order.
1. Monroe
2. Arthur
3. Truman
4. Reagan
5. Taylor
6. Wilson
7. Hoover
8. Carter
9. Alaska
10. Hawaii
11. Kansas
12. Oregon
13. Nevada
14. Denver
15. Boston

16. statue
17. Senate
18. united
19. states
20. Tubman
21. Barton
22. pledge

Page 71
1. true
2. false (James Madison)
3. false (Betsy Ross)
4. true
5. false (more red than white)
6. true
7. true
8. false (Jefferson or five-dollar)
9. true
10. false (Yuri Gagarin)
11. true
12. true
13. false (Civil War or 1776)
14. true
15. false (Abraham Lincoln)